A Long Ti

Snapshots of Life in the

South Wales Valleys

David West

First published 2014
By Rowanvale Books
57, Brynllwchwr Road,
Loughor,
Swansea
SA4 6SQ
www.rowanvalebooks.com

A CIP catalogue record for this book is available from
the British Library.
ISBN 978-0-9573183-7-3

Dedication

For three women who have given me Life and Love: my mother, Joyce, my mother-in-law Elsie, and my soul mate and wife, my Cariad,[1] Sheila.

---

[1] Cariad: Welsh meaning `love'.

CONTENTS

Acknowledgments   i

Introduction   1

The First Time - Cyfarthfa 1997   7

Ancestors Within   15

Road to Enlightenment   29

Y Mynydd   37

Ambition   45

Mandy   53

Deadly Dai   63

The Loot   70

Acknowledgements

Throughout the 'long time coming' of these stories, I have been blessed with loyal Merthyr friends who, often unwittingly, supply material to write about. Adrian and Illtyd (both Sullivan but not 'belonging'[2]) are also cycling buddies and such good friends that they ate most of my grapes on the way to visit me in hospital. In addition to having been a cycling mentor since my first falls and pukes, Adrian does many of my chores from next door (such as potentially dangerous hedge-cutting and pre-dawn rubbish and recycling disposal) leaving me more time to 'research' and go through the motions of writing. Illtyd knows about the natural environment and 'wildlife' in general, including the local population, and his 'epics' occasionally feature himself as a character not unlike Mr Bean[3]. Like Adrian and Illtyd, Haydn Jones has been an unceasing friend in all weathers and he too is a treasure trove of local knowledge and stories. Such is his constancy that he has undertaken to buy a copy of my little book so '…at least you'll sell one!' What more can I say about some of the special friendships I value so greatly in Merthyr? Well, I'll tell you: If they said something nice to me I'd worry.

---

[2] Belonging': Valleys dialectic meaning family or related. Mind you, if I was related to either of them I wouldn't admit it either.

[3] Illtyd is sometimes known to his long-suffering wife Ann and the rest of his family as Mr Bean for reasons which you can probably imagine - although there might well be another book on the way

Sheila (known affectionately as 'Scot'[4]), my wife, is also a Merthyr girl born and partly bred, and she encouraged me to seek publication for these stories, which would otherwise have languished in the binary corridors of my laptop forever. I am also grateful to Scot for her patient and thorough proof reading and proficient word processing skills. Without her I am certainly less!

More objective proofreading has been undertaken by Brian Cole (next door) and Joanna Sullivan (the sensible one next door on the other side) to whom I am also grateful.

I have benefitted greatly from the enthusiasm, patience and time afforded me by the local school-teacher and historian Christine Thomas, who walked many miles around the relics and monuments that attest to Merthyr Tydfil's historical past.

The staff at Merthyr Tydfil and Dowlais Libraries gave me their guidance and support in the early days of my local research and, in this respect, Caroline Jacobs was particularly resourceful and helpful.

As she so often does, Gaynor Thomas provided family support to enable a weekend away. This time it was to escape distraction so there would be no excuse for me not finishing this little book. Gaynor has also permitted me to use a tongue-in-cheek comedic 'letter of appreciation' called 'The Loot', which I sent her some years ago.

---

[4] Her father being a betting man, Sheila was named after the 1948 Grand National winner - a horse called *Sheila's Cottage*. Courtesy of my perverse brand of humour, she became affectionately known as *Scottage* which inevitably became *Scot* for short. But I'm sure the astute reader had already worked this out.

My brother Michael once said of a short story I'd written, that it had 'stayed in his head'. That appreciation from a lifelong friend stayed in my head and encouraged me to persevere with my creative writing.

In addition to repeated surgery due to ancient sports' injuries, I suffer the anxieties and depressions of bipolar disorder. My quality of life - and whatever creativity can be associated with it in the good times - is also so very much better thanks to the considerate patience and professionalism of my General Medical Practitioner, Dr. Sally Hosen.

Finally, I owe thanks to Cat, Sarah and the team at Rowanvale Books for their encouragement, patience and support for generally inspiring some greater confidence.

A Long Time Coming:

Snapshots of Life in the South Wales Valleys

David West

Introduction

I began writing in my late teens. Some twenty years later, all my material along with a large and diverse collection of books and a family heirloom was stolen at a time when I was already experiencing low personal ebb. Ebbs and flows have been a feature of my life and, whilst I don't aspire to their talent, I am comforted that many famously creative people have also suffered a lifetime of ebbing and flowing. Mood and anxiety disorders have underpinned their lives too and they have been, like me, bipolar – for periods of time 'touched with fire', and at other times confused and destabilised by a lethal combination of anxiety and debilitating depression.

This little book of short stories has been *A Long Time Coming* with interruptions for periods of working long hours sometimes away from home, and periods of inability to even imagine there being sunshine or creativity in life. Each of these stories has some basis in truth and there is a gradual reduction of earnestness with each story. The final three culminate this pattern with, first, the satirical but comic message that is 'Mandy', then the slapstick comedy of 'Deadly Dai' and the general silliness and slapstick of the final tongue-in-cheek 'letter of appreciation' called 'The Loot'.

Shortly after 31 August 1997, when Diana Princess of Wales died so tragically, I wrote 'The First Time - Cyfarthfa 1997'. This story won the 1997 Charles Jones Short Story Competition in Merthyr Tydfil and helped renew my enthusiasm for creative writing. In Cyfarthfa Park I had seen a dead bird and a young woman with her mother and two children. I reflected on the impermanence of life and my experiences of working with people challenged and often undermined by social problems and, in many cases, affected and afflicted, sometimes terminally, by drugs and crime. I tried to place myself behind her eyes in a life she might have – hence the 'stream of consciousness' of the narrative voice.

'Ancestors Within' contains historical truths with undertones of the evolution of life and death. It contains heartfelt enquiry into the hope and learning of young and old offset against the harsh realities of lost lives and damaged relationships. 'Belonging' in the Welsh valleys means related to by family. We all belong to the same family, and pebbles of love and compassion dropped into the impermanent pond of life can create infinite ripples. This story takes us back to the time when Merthyr Tydfil was the 'iron and steel capital of the world', with manufacturing barons obtaining great wealth at the expense of the workers who toiled long hours for poor pay and endured appalling living conditions.

Adversity and romance, emotional turmoil, lust and longing interact and conflict in 'Road to Enlightenment' - partly inspired by my work with people with disabilities. Standing amongst a small, surprised audience in a Merthyr Tydfil public house one Christmas, I had tears in my eyes as I listened to the spontaneous, sweet and powerful singing talents of a young woman with profound physical and learning disabilities. This story is about the treasury of special abilities and qualities, which often remain trapped and unexpressed. These people and those who sincerely love and care were (and probably still are) insufficiently supported. People with learning and physical disabilities can teach us so much if we listen.

'Y Mynydd' is Welsh for 'The Mountain', and was inspired during instructive walks I took with Christine Thomas, a Merthyr Tydfil school teacher and local historian, and the mental pictures I was able to paint from this and other research into local history. This included the life, reflected in this story, of Charles Jones, a local author and poet. Love for the land, poetry and romantic love; a man who has a sense of the end of his physical life looks back and reflects on his life story in his enduring homeland in the Welsh valleys.

'Ambition' is set in South Wales, but has its basis in my own experience of working for the probation service, in social work and other therapeutic settings in various parts of England, Northern Ireland and Wales. Many people who work within a therapeutic setting are sensitive and vulnerable human beings. They must use their empathy with wisdom and judgment in adverse situations that cross social and professional boundaries.

The last three stories of this book reflect an off-centre look at personal and local life. Laughing at my anxiety-fuelled, absent-minded and often distracted clumsiness and impracticability is perhaps a coping strategy for Sheila, my wife – a good way to accommodate the truth of it. Sometimes we laugh affectionately with and at those around us, and I believe it can reinforce our bonding – starting with our grandchildren who love to laugh. If I am formal and polite - 'nice' to my Sheila - her usual response is: 'What do you want?' I might reply, 'I don't want anything.' In this case she will inevitably conclude: 'Well, what have you done then?' Best stick with the humour!

My mother-in-law Elsie used to work in the local Co-operative store (known as the Co-op) and her misuse of the English language, including her unique answers to crossword clues, has become legendary within the family and beyond. She is someone I love and respect; someone who has been through the very worst that life can throw at her but who retains the ability to laugh at herself through her many trials and tribulations. 'Mandy' is loosely based on Elsie and is a fun look at the use and interpretation of language in everyday life - with some parody with Mrs Malaprop in Sheridan's 'The Rivals'. And, lest I forget the plot: your life can change when you least expect it!

Just before Christmas 1997 we moved into a neglected one hundred-years'-old house in Merthyr Tydfil, and our kind neighbours are now amongst our closest and dearest of friends. In those early days the borrowing of ladders was vital and 'Deadly Dai' was inspired when I put my foot through the shed roof en-route to the ladders. 'The Loot' is a tongue in cheek letter of thanks to Gaynor Thomas, a lifelong friend of my wife and a true friend to both of us who, consistent with her intrinsic constancy, attended a crisis (yet another created by my capricious memory) at short notice. The engagement of tradesmen was vital at the time this was written and the letter of apology represents an embellished picture of something that really happened on the day I collected my prize cheque for the Charles Jones Short Story Competition.

When Horace Charles Jones sponsored the short story competition in Merthyr Tydfil, he knew he was dying of cancer and he asked me to write his biography. I spent many hours with him and, subsequent to his death, with his wife and daughter and people who knew him, I researched his work in the Merthyr Tydfil Library. But I could not obtain a publisher because, despite his talent and his intriguing biography, he was insufficiently well known outside his own home town. This seems to be in the nature of publishing in a commercial world. When Rowanvale Books accepted these short stories they did something extraordinary: they asked me about my inspiration and sources, and they referred to the narrative style of my writing – some things I had never thought about before!

It took a while to learn that when someone in the Welsh Valleys prefaces what they are about to say with 'I've got to be honest' (each syllable hitting high and low notes alternately), then you can be fairly certain that what is about to be said will either be colourfully embroidered or will stretch the boundaries of truth. If they preface something with 'I'm not being funny' (again with alternate high and low notes), gird your loins because, believe me, they're about to be 'funny', and not in the humorous sense. If someone says, for example, they will be somewhere or do something 'now in a minute', this cannot be translated as 'now' nor 'in a minute', but at some indeterminate time in the future, if at all. I hope this helps non-local readers to understand some of the dialectical peculiarities of Merthyr Tydfil and the South Wales Valleys.

The First Time - Cyfarthfa 1997

…won't be long now. Just stay calm. Why did I have to get here first?

It must be almost time though. Let's have another look. Fifteen minutes, give or take. What did they say … five or ten minutes either way? Funny thing, last time I was here a couple of teenage boys … in those loose sort of jeans and trainers and stuff they wear … they were walking … well, almost running really … towards the park exit at the Cefn end and we passed them going the other way, me and Mam … before the stroke.

Anyway, next thing … a man with a black uniform and a job to do … one of the security men I suppose … came out of Cyfarthfa Castle asking if we'd seen these two boys and where they'd gone. They'd been sort of grinning and polite, these boys, when they passed and I remember saying 'hello' or something. I'm not being funny but I felt a bit sort of suspicious of them then. You know, young boys going out of their way to be friendly and polite. They don't seem to do it any more … well, most young boys I know anyway … Turns out I was right.

There's someone coming through the main gate and he's coming up the hill towards me. He doesn't seem to be looking this way. Looks as if he could be wearing an anorak ... I can't see the colour from here. Wait a minute, he's got a dog on a lead. Nobody said anything about a dog.

False alarm... Mind you, I suppose he could be bringing a dog. That's not an anorak anyway by the look... No, that's not an anorak, and he's probably just walking the dog, probably does it every day ... especially if he's not working. He's going the other way anyway ... taking the dog up the top fields.

Come on girl, relax; just be patient for another five or ten minutes at the outside. Just hang on. What are you getting yourself in a state for?

The previous time we came up here, the time before we saw those two boys who'd been up to no good, we'd come up to Cyfarthfa Castle - me and Mam and the boys - to look round the museum and there was an old Hoover washing machine there just like the one Mam's still got. We had a laugh about that. I think it was the first time I'd seen Mam laugh since Dad died. Not that she had much to laugh about before he died. Still, mustn't talk ill of the dead. He's only up in Cefn Cemetery and who knows?

There's a car coming in. Let's see, how many people in it ... if it's only one, it could be him. No, they said he'd be walking and... I suppose he could be walking..., after he's got out of his car and..., this is a car park, after all's said and done... No, it's just an old man and his wife in the car anyway. Probably going to just sit and look ... maybe read a bit, do some crosswords, sleep, who knows?

I've kept remembering, ever since that time with the washing machine ... that dove..., or pigeon whatever it was, lying on the floor just up from here. Over there where they park the cars ... with its head crushed and its neck broken. Just can't get it out of my mind. Somebody must have reversed over it whilst it was feeding. You'd think people would be careful where there are lots of birds feeding. They're much nicer to look at anyway, the birds ... in the park, than lots of cars polluting all over the place. Poor thing, it was beautiful and it looked as if it could have been quite young - even dead it was sort of lovely somehow with its silky looking feathers all kind of fanning and fluffing in the wind.

I wonder if anyone's ever fired that big old gun. It looks good stood there outside the castle. I wonder if it's ever been used, if anyone's ever killed anyone with it.

It can't be long now. I suppose I'm bound to be nervous on my first time.

It'll probably be my last time too for this. I wonder if he knows it's my first time. First times are always difficult. Then it gets easier. I remember the first time...

There's a young couple strolling with their arms around each other. It's nice to see young people in love, touching each other and strolling through the autumn leaves. They look as if they're laughing and joking with each other and... kissing, maybe. What are they doing now? They're lighting up cigarettes ... and he's just spat on the floor. Why do they do that? Why do youngsters spit? Even the girls seem to do it nowadays..., and the language. Now he's throwing something ... chucking something away ... on the floor ... amongst the leaves.

Two minutes to go. I'm in the right place. Don't worry if he's five or ten minutes either side. Just make sure you're in the right place and wearing the blue and white scarf and carrying the matching bag. I wonder what he'll look like.

James is beginning to look like a young man and he's only eleven. Mind, his father was tall, as far as I can remember from what little I saw of him. Between him and Dad they could have kept a brewery going on their own. Young Richard worries me though. He seems so small for his age. I mean, he's nine now and so nervous. His teacher says he lacks concentration. Some days it's as if he's elsewhere in his mind. Still, he seems happy enough, I've got to be honest.

What if this is a ... what-you-call-it? What if I'm being stood up or whatever, a set-up or something? Don't lose your nerve now. You've thought it out before.

I know both the boys worry about me and that can't be good for them. They shouldn't have to worry about making ends meet; not at their age. If we had a man it would be different. Why the hell should we need a man! They're only good for ... Well, I suppose there is that ... a bit of comfort now and again wouldn't go astray. You just can't trust them though can you?

Come on, stretch the legs but stay close to the bench. It can't be long now. Show yourself confidently ... that means no doubts.

What's happening? It's a quarter past and there's only been that man with his dog.

They're fishing over there, those men. Perhaps they're shift-workers ... or just a few more of Merthyr's Army of Unemployed. Funny thing, though ... most of them drink like fish rather than go fishing. The ones who go fishing are the ones who are happy. I've got to be honest, the ones who haven't got a job are the ones who seem to drink for Wales.

That's what happened with him … led to his going…, he said he was looking for work. Perhaps he was but where did that leave me and the boys? He never sent anything back and we don't even know where he is now - except with another woman and his guts full of alcohol.

I can feel my heart beating fast now. I thought I was going to be in control through all this. They said don't worry. I told them I'd gone past worrying about anything. You've just got to get on with your life, haven't you? Who's going to look after me and the kids if I don't? Now they're talking about giving you something to do with one hand … and somewhere for the kids to go … and taking your money off you with the other. I'm not being funny but it's a big con trick if you ask me … and in any case what pleasures have I got in life?

The park seems so empty. Still, it is a Tuesday. It's going to be twenty-past soon. That man's put his dog back on the lead and he's … he's going the other way, out of the park. Sit back down on the bench, girl, and be patient. It feels even more uncomfortable this time and I'm getting a cold bum. Better stay put or he'll miss me. There just doesn't seem to be anyone about.

Someone … a man in a blue anorak is coming up the driveway. Yes, the hood is up. Here we go…, this is it…, everything ready. Carry a handbag but don't use it. Stand up so he can see you… There's something about the way he bounces on his toes. He's getting much closer quite quickly now. Don't panic. He'll take the hood down when he's a bit closer … about twenty yards away. And that will be the signal to start walking so that he can be sure who you are.

11

My mother's had a stroke. I can't stop her smoking and I'm sure our James is starting to experiment. Still, they give them plenty of education about drugs at school. I look at Mum sometimes and I can't believe she's belonging to me. She's gone to look so old and that cough. Why won't she listen? Still, she's been smoking for years and years ... had her first one when she was twelve I think she said. They all did it in those days and I suppose it's hard then...

He's taking the hood down and coming towards me.

Seems very spritely for a... Oh, my God... Oh, my God... He's just a boy ..., a child..., a little boy..., somebody's son... Dear God, what am I doing? I'm frozen. My breath is all white in the cold air. Where's the stuff... No, where's the gate? Got to get out... I'll throw the stuff in the bin... He might be following me... That child..., that little boy..., he might be following me... I could be his mother... I'll chuck it somewhere else..., on the floor, amongst the leaves..., in that bin by the gate... as soon as I get there... Oh, God, I'm so unhappy. This wasn't supposed to happen... No, I'll take it home...

Yes, I'll take it home.

Ancestors Within

As wide-eyed curious children we ask where we came from. Within us are the mysteries and treasures of who we are. Our Ancestors live on amongst us and within us; the burdens and gifts of humanity - we pass them on to our children.

The chill shivered down my back and neck. It was a fresh autumn morning in the warmth of a book-walled room in the Dowlais Library in Merthyr Tydfil - the former iron and steel capital of the world. In that local history room with its 'smack-on-the-hand' quietness, every hair on my arms and upper back tugged at my chilled skin. My pen felt cold and wet in my taut, trembling fingers and I looked around the room. A large oil painting on the wall, donated by a family of former steelworkers, illustrated the Dowlais Ironworks and the blinding glow of the iron ore in the coke ovens.

I was mesmerized by what had just happened. I walked across the scarred and pitted wood-tiled polish-smelling room, scanning the regiments of books for more seductive human shadows that move like amoeba. Through the swinging double-doors I drifted into the corridor. I crossed the hallway and went through the gaping entrance to the pavement outside and the haze of the morning sun setting fire to a crisp, autumn-chilled Saturday morning. I soon felt refreshed and I returned with renewed focus, my every footstep feeling the solid floor to the local history room where I could return to my present-day world of reading and writing.

1862 Population of Merthyr district 49,794 persons with 10,634 houses inhabited. Dowlais had over 10,000 people living there, average wage for skilled workmen 24/2d. Flour 43/- per sack, potatoes 5/ 8d per cwt, beef 5-1/2d per lb, bacon 7d per lb, tea 4/- per lb Profit £3,059 for year.

These were difficult times for the foundry workers, who had lived in appalling conditions just a short distance from this library. Suddenly my skin felt the pore-prickling damp chill again, low down on my back this time; it ran up my spine and across my shoulders as the shelves and books seemed to disappear into the shadowy background. He was there again, as if he belonged to this place. He wore filthy industrial clothing and moved purposefully, his glowing eyes reflecting energy, strength and determination. He walked across the room in front of me and stooped forward; his face glowed as he worked with his partially gloved hands. I could not see what he was doing but I felt heat radiating towards me and I could smell sulphur. He walked back again into the shadows and disappeared. I was confused and yet excited as I looked around the empty room, my pen poised in my paralysed hand and my disbelieving eyes staring at that place, which now revealed only shelves full of books. I hunched my shoulders and shuddered.

A notice on the wall dated AD1840 says that Sir Josiah John Guest of the Dowlais Iron Works and Thomas Evans, of the same place,

should and lawfully might make, use, exercise, and vend their Invention of Certain Improvements in the Manufacture of Iron and Other Metals ... and send their greeting to her Present Most Excellent Majesty Queen Victoria ... bearing date Westminster, the Twenty-eighth day of May, in the third year of her reign.

I remembered my Dowlais friends and their families talking, and the names like Guest, Evans and Lewis spat out with acerbic distaste.

From outside I heard the noise of vehicle engines rising and falling as they negotiated the hills and junctions. I seemed to be leaving a dream and returning to the twenty-first century. It had felt almost like my mind had left my body and entered another time. Whatever had happened, I had to take hold and think clearly. What had triggered this episode, which was surely not just a creation of my turbulent mind? I remembered my mother relating her 'psychic' experience during a picnic in the Forest of Dean. She said she had 'found herself' in a medieval village amongst its inhabitants. I felt she must have fallen asleep and dreamt it but she insisted it was a real and vivid experience, even describing their clothing and environment in detail. Perhaps, I thought, this is something else I have inherited – a psychic awareness, something I had never believed could exist.

I was about to collect up my books and leave the library and he was there again, the same man – or apparition - right in front of me. This time the shape of a small child appeared from the shadows behind him and the smell of sulphur was unmistakeable. I could not have imagined that. The atmosphere was poisonous and I felt nauseous as the dark, shadowy figures passed across the library. They stopped for a moment, and looked, knowingly and almost disdainfully, straight at me. The boy looked at me, and I knew the hatred in his unseeing eyes. The two moved away resignedly and disappeared into the shadows.

The small child had reminded me of my eldest son Jamie, when he was small and I still knew him. He looked so familiar and I found my obsessive ruminating taking me over again. Jamie is still here amidst the summer and winter and history and future but I will never know him again. All those years of paternal poverty and deprivation can never be reclaimed.

In 1866 Dowlais employed 781 females in total, 1,432 males, 297 females under 18 years of age including nine boys and one girl under 10 years of age, 505 boys and 164 girls from 10-13 years of age, 968 boys and 233 girls from 14 to 18 years of age. Fourth cholera outbreak in Merthyr district (the last), profit £62,502 for year.

'Is everything OK?' The librarian, returning a book to the shelves, materialised from nowhere.

'Yes, OK,' I said, after a slightly startled split second. I think she said something about the time of year and a bug that's 'doing the rounds'. Whether she was suggesting it might have been afflicting me at this time I don't know but I think someone from within me answered her. She must have walked so close to this man and the small child and yet I sensed she could never have seen or collided with them. Then, another female voice in the distance with a lyrical Merthyr accent: she'd 'been at the doctor's' and she 'had to have some tests ... all this rain; you can tell the winter's on the way again with all this flu and colds going round; Meurig's off work'... and so on. I was back in today.

I struggled, as if from sleep, to return to that autumn Saturday morning. The smell of sulphur was replaced with the warm atmosphere with occasional light draughts of cool air as the main door opened and closed. I looked at the regiments of books lined up around the walls as far as I could see and the well-trodden wood-tiled floors.

But I knew I had smelt the sulphur; it was mixed with the sense of strength in the smell of hot iron ore and my nose had felt raw inside with the fumes and the heat. This was not just about what I saw; it was about the whole experience of actually being in that place, in the place where these people worked.

I tried to return to the local information in front of me and I looked down at the writing pad I had made a start on. The pad contained my own notes but I was shocked to see pages of pictures and notes, which had a familiar child-like style. My chest thumping hard and my throat tight, I found it hard to breath. I could not remember writing this much; I had only been there for ten or fifteen minutes, or so I thought. I looked at my watch. I had been there for two hours.

I looked around again, not really expecting anything. Had I really seen that shadowy figure, not floating, as in many ghost stories, but walking around the room? I pulled books and papers together and prepared to leave. I was trembling a little so I sat for a moment. I put my head in my hands and tried to think. I knew it could have been another of my 'episodes', which can involve unbridled imagination and even hallucination, but this had been more real and vivid than anything before. My ruminations set in again: 'I loved and respected my father despite many things. When he died I knew there were many relationship years lost forever'. I loved Jamie too and, when they sent me from the delivery suite to remove the cord from around his neck, I didn't know what to do with myself. I was the proverbial pacing parent until I heard the miraculous cry of a new-born baby. Not many years later he was gone for good.

I looked up and the child was in front of me, staring from beneath his filthy cap. He was five or six years old but his tired, black-faced gaze was sombre and mature. He looked accusingly, and I sensed we were being watched. The man could only be the child's father, his face seemingly enraged by the flashing furnace fires as if the mural had come to life. Then the two walked away into the darting shadows of the massive foundry, and the flashing fires and heat were replaced with the quiet peacefulness of the Dowlais Library on an autumn morning.

I looked down at the table to anchor myself in the literature. It told me that parents brought children to work in these iron and steel foundries for extra money. If a collier or puddler employed his boy to assist him he could receive extra pay, which economic circumstances forced most of them to do. Officially the companies all disapproved of this exploitative and dangerous practice but they did nothing to prevent it. Then I thought I heard a whisper: 'You left me, you should have been there'.

I returned to my home in a dream. I sat in my room and tried to organise my thoughts. My notebook sat on the table in front of me and I turned the page.

The monster blast furnaces – of which there were six - reached a height of seventy or eighty feet, with a diameter of between eighteen and twenty feet and reached blast temperatures of between one thousand and fourteen hundred degrees Fahrenheit. The immense scale of these works is difficult to imagine. The Iron Works at Dowlais blazed a wide trail of technical advancement and production innovations and its men, machines and reputation extended throughout the world to wherever iron and steel was made.

I looked again at my note pad and, turning back the page, I saw the scribbles of a child; pictures, and a child's attempts at writing his name. It began with 'J' and I could make out some of the shapes on the mural on the wall of the library. Sometimes we daydream and it can seem quite real, but this was different. I was terrified and excited at the same time and I felt as if it was somehow a part of my routine. I had felt the anger, the heat, the vibrancy and the poverty of this foundry environment. My attitude and demeanour, my whole being, had seemed to change as I became one with the people and the foundry. I was not visiting; I belonged there. I was unable to work out how I could have sensed all these things in a way that gave rise to such a vivid experience. Words seem insufficient to describe to you how I experienced all these things. I could not forget what I had experienced and I felt compelled to go to work at the Dowlais Foundry. I felt I was living a dream and I had to see it through – because there had been gross injustices and lies and poverty and deprivation of children from their parents, and parents from their children.

On an early autumn evening I left my home. Now it's my turn; I will retrieve this nightmare and bring it safely back to safety and truth. I could see down the hill in the distance a red furnace-glare lighting the skies from as far as Hirwaun and all around Merthyr Tydfil. I was in a real and vibrant dream in a different historical time, and I could hear the clatter and clash of the echoing foundry. It was a chill evening and I seemed to drift, and yet I was hurrying to be there. I felt the cool black dust-ridden breeze on my face. In the distance below me, the immense fires coming from the brightly glowing sites of the Plymouth, Cyfarthfa and Penydarren Ironworks, all flashing in the black night as I hurriedly made my dream-like way up the hill the short distance towards the Dowlais Ironworks – seemingly in another time.

The livid hue was ghastly on the faces of the workmen. The dirty sweat beads ran down my forehead and the back of my neck from beneath my cap. The sounds of steam rolling mills and mass hammers worked by machines or wielded by brawny filthy arms didn't allow for any talking; you just could not be heard. The pall of smoke and fumes overhanging the area were overwhelming, as was the heat. My shoulders and back were soaking wet; even my legs were running with perspiration, and I was thirsty. Banks of furnaces stood against higher ground which supported the charging platforms. Furnaces were being fed from above, slag and molten iron tapped-off at their base. I heard a scream and I had a real sense of the danger of this environment.

The shadowy dream-figure of the young boy walked in to this 'other' life of mine again, from somewhere in the shadows. There followed another boy and a girl of similar age and then there were lots of shadowy figures in this dark and flashing hell-fire environment, seemingly ignoring me. I found myself in a huge area with deafening noise and heat and fumes. My unaccustomed nose burned inside and my eyes streamed in the unmistakeable atmosphere of hot sulphur. I was soaked in perspiration, I felt dirty and I could feel the dust in my throat.

The face of the boy with blond curls creeping around the band of his dirty brown peaked cap glowed as he looked at me with hatred and defiance. He started to walk away and he looked back over his shoulder. This time it was unmistakeable, a tired and resigned look that seemed to whisper beneath of pleading. He drifted away into the flashing blackness and joined a larger figure whom I felt could have been my father too; and I also realised he could have been me and those memorable words 'You're just like your father' seemed to whisper a memory to me.

Flames from the hot coke leapt from the oven and ignited molten iron descending from above. The boy was enveloped in a flame as his clothing ignited. He shouted for help and then he screamed, but his terrified agony-stricken shrieks could not penetrate the deafening echoes of the clattering foundry works. This immense slashing and clanging and hissing monster seemed to stand over this tragedy like a satisfied glutton belching out filth. I was paralysed. I could not move; I looked for the boy's father but could not see him anywhere. I somehow knew he would not be there when he was needed.

I was paralysed by fear and helplessness and I stared in abject horror. I wanted to throw myself at the flames but I seemed to be held back by shadowy people. They knew, as I did, that I could not approach the child because I, too, would become one with molten iron. I just wanted to wake up somewhere away from this dreadful hell. I was sobbing helplessly as I turned away from the flames leaping from his coke-dirty clothing and from the writhing, blackening body of a young boy who should have had the whole of his life ahead of him. The emergency response seemed routine and barely concerned about the death of a child. His father had disappeared and I just did not want to be here any longer. I could not understand why nobody noticed me. Everything was familiar and yet nothing seemed real.

I felt myself floating home through the semi-dark cold dampness of the fresh and brand new early morning. Through the familiar dark desolation and cloudiness of my loss I saw the neighbouring Penydarren works down the valley with Plymouth just beyond. In the direction of the Brecon Beacons, smoke and flame was rising from Crawshay's 'Cyfarthfa', the greatest industrial plant in existence, together with its associated 'Ynysfach' works. Merthyr Tydfil was, in truth, the iron-making capital of the world, but at what cost?

Until today, I have not told anyone of these experiences, which were recorded in my note book. Whilst it seems extraordinary, and I have no expectation that anyone will believe me, it was somehow an experience that belonged to me and to this child and a father – all fathers perhaps. It was an experience that served as a reminder of something, rather than anything extraordinary. It was, perhaps, something I deserved because of who I am. I just don't know how to explain it any differently. The following morning it was as if nothing had happened.

In the next couple of months, the memory was beginning to fade a little and take up a place in my mind where it no longer troubled me. Then I attended Dowlais Junior Mixed School to watch a Christmas concert. I sat in the front row and began to enjoy the musical show, the talents of these children as they acted out the Nativity – the Christian belief in the coming of the Infant Child of the Father of all Mankind. There was some humour, and really good individual and group performances from these little children. There were also some performances in which children dressed up in traditional costumes from Merthyr Tydfil's historical past, including the era of iron and steel. I glanced around the hall and there were examples of the children's work on one of the walls to my right. A heavy feeling descended into my stomach and spread around my chest as I received the shock of incredulous recognition. One of the sheets of paper contained a number of child's drawings – each of which I recognised.

The teachers had obviously worked hard with the children but, from the very start, there was one child who disrupted. He pestered and interfered with the other children as they tried to perform. I was continuously distracted as this child pestered and grabbed and giggled and kicked. The young teacher repeatedly failed to deal with him. 'Stop it; behave; I'll stand you on the table.'

'For goodness sake,' I thought. 'Get a grip of him; he's a diabolical nuisance and he's spoiling the whole thing for everyone.' Then he turned and looked straight at me with a suggestion of a grin. He seemed to search my face and, with that familiar defiant look, his blond hair curling around the band of his brown peaked cap, there was an unmistakeable threat to do something shocking, and I was now riveted to the sight of him.

I felt the chill at the nape of my neck and my upper back; I was wet with perspiration and yet my skin felt cold. I knew in that moment that those blue eyes with a touch of hazel were those that had seen inside me. His patient and caring teacher tenderly picked him up and, still concentrating on the performance of the other children, placed this hyperactive and rebellious child gently and meaningfully on her lap. He settled placidly and, almost serenely, placed his head against her woolly shoulder so that his peaked cap tilted comically above his now credulous porcelain face. He laid his cherubic little miniature hand, with its smears of theatrical soot, across her maternal chest, and he was peaceful. I felt proud of his young teacher for being there for him unconditionally.

The minibus with the printing on the side returned me to my home. Later that day I had some visitors. Another little boy was amongst them. He looked very similar but was dressed in a school uniform.

'Grampy,' he said looking straight at me with those very same searching blue eyes with a touch of hazel.

'Yes?' I said, when I became aware that this familiar child was in reality addressing me.

'When are you going to be better enough to teach history again?'

My room seemed to have a new emptiness and yet, from deep within my turbulent mind, came a sense of future and of possibility.

Road to Enlightenment

The flower that blooms in adversity is the rarest and most beautiful of all.
Walt Disney Company, Mulan (Pictureback) 2005

As Julie reached for the microphone, Stephen felt her firm breast against his arm. The flutter of excitement that paralysed his breathing was numbed by a pang of guilt. He thought fleetingly of the loss he had suffered of his marital relationship, and the persistent mental picture appeared again of the late-night car crash, two years ago, which had left his journalist wife seriously injured. Then, with accomplished routine, he pulled the curtains of his mind's eye on this part of his life.

The Restoration Hotel had been chosen for its wheelchair access. Stephen had been involved with disabled children since his younger brother, who had cerebral palsy, had died in an epileptic seizure at seven years of age. It was a cruel twist of fate that Sarah, his wife, had her legs crushed in the car crash and had become disabled after less than six months of their marriage. Stephen and Julie, along with parents, carers and volunteers, were preparing for the Christmas party the following week. There was anticipation and great excitement and Stephen, a photographer, was already snapping.

Julie was a slim and attractive single parent of a child, Jessica, who had cerebral palsy and learning difficulties. Slightly buxom with medium length dark hair and piercing almost black eyes framed in light eyeshadow, Julie had reddened lips and she was wearing a crimson suit and white blouse revealing a discrete cleavage. Stephen resisted the temptation to pursue this apparently easy-going attractive friend as another photographic opportunity.

'You haven't said how Sarah is these days, and it's over a year since we've seen her,' she said almost apologetically. His eyes stared at nothing.

'She's lost interest in the group,' he said. 'She's lost interest in everything'. He turned and looked into Julie's benevolent smile without seeing. 'I have to do everything,' he said absently. At that moment someone called to Julie, asking her to give a hand in the kitchen.

A quiet understanding had developed between Stephen and Julie. Their friendship was inspired and sustained by their misfortune and loss - perceived gaps in their lives caused by disability. It was reinforced by the mutual interest in photographic opportunities that Julie's style, attractiveness and wistful interest in a modelling career presented. This latter interest, said Julie, was out of her reach. The commitment required was just not compatible with the support she felt bound to provide for Jessica at every opportunity.

Throughout the next week, Stephen recalled this encounter with Julie. He looked at the many photographs he had taken of the group, which had included her, and he admired those that he had taken of

Julie for herself as an emblematic image of a career which she would like to have. He experienced phantom sensations of her breast against his arm, and he looked forward to the party. At the end of each day's freelance photography work, he threw himself as always into domestic tasks. Routinely, he would not notice and neither would he hear that, in reality, Sarah had already done these jobs. At the end of the evening he would retire alone to his single bed, leaving Sarah to her reading, her crochet and her writing, some of it about disability and, he believed, her unremitting un-happiness.

Julie's daughter Jessica surprised everyone. Twelve years of age, confined to a wheelchair and twisted with cerebral palsy, the energy of her soprano singing aroused the whole spirit of the party. Stephen held the karaoke microphone in front of her and she responded with vocal power and musical accuracy. Stephen could barely conceal his grief for this child who could make such a wonderful sound but could neither speak well nor understand the words. When Jessica wasn't singing, her belly laugh and ecstatic smile exuded intense and humble joy and thanks. Stephen knew that Jessica attended a day centre and lived occasionally in a community home supported constantly by carers so that her mother could have some respite from her care. He pondered on her quality of life and her experience of family life.

Just for once Julie seemed to be letting her hair down. She had even danced a little in time to Jessica's singing. Stephen felt some concern for her, not having seen her drink so much wine and, indeed, not being able to afford to do so with her limited income. She had worked so hard for others organising and supporting this and other events; perhaps she deserved a little enjoyment herself.

At the end of the evening, the transport, adapted for people with disabilities, arrived. Stephen felt sadness again for Jessica and those who were forced throughout their lives to depend on the goodwill of others. He wondered why Julie did not seem to notice or to appreciate the courage, spontaneity and the talent of her daughter. With support and encouragement Jessica could do so much more for herself, he thought. But Julie had given birth to this child; she had always been there and had probably seen it all before. He imagined Julie had created for herself a public image of being inviolable, but was lonely and quietly suffering inside. He remembered Julie telling him she had no wish to possess her daughter as she felt her own mother had selfishly done for her own sake, but to allow Jessica to be whom and what she wanted to for herself to the extent that she was able.

Whilst driving Julie home, he began to feel heady in the spell of her perfume. He had flashback pictures in his head to another clear December night two years ago. The accident itself had not been his fault. The driver in the other vehicle had been drinking heavily. The young boy had been driving a stolen vehicle dangerously and he too was now disabled for life. It would not have happened if Stephen had not been driving his wife from that party. It would not have happened if he had not taken her. It was a Photographic Society party and nothing to do with journalism; she would not have been there were it not for him! He caught sight of Julie's thigh against the hemline of her raised skirt. He felt aroused - then a paroxysm of flashback fear gripped him. His eyes darted back to the road. It was clear and deserted. The blood had drained from his skin, he could feel his heart beating and the lights seemed to have illuminated the crisp night more brightly than before.

In Julie's untidy terraced home Stephen felt like an awkward teenager. In real life the lofty fantasies he had entertained with Julie began to dissolve. But Julie brushed against him as she threw her coat on the settee. She turned to face him and the mutual attraction was physical. The top buttons of her blouse had become undone and she moved her hand as if to correct this mistake. Stephen impulsively intercepted her hand; he took it in his and she moved closer to him into an embraceable position. Instinctively he enveloped her and kissed her waiting lips. Her response was immediate and passionate. His palms moved from her perfect hips to feel the hooks and eyes of her bra strap through the silky smooth texture of her blouse. She was passionate and persuasive but he pulled back; he saw her flushed face; her shining, expectant eyes and her moist and vital rouged mouth, which moments before had been searching and pleading.

His heart saw beyond her immediate image. He saw Jessica, her disabled daughter, as the child Sarah had not had. His eyes drifted down her unimpaired body to the floor.

'I'm sorry,' he said. 'I'm really sorry. I can't do this. I'm not the right person for you. It's not your fault.' He picked up his coat and, fumbling urgently in the pockets for his keys, he left.

Inside the house Julie sat down; she wept a little and then she picked herself up, swilled her face with cold water and reapplied her make-up before moving to the mirror and approving of the image before her. Outside, Stephen looked up at the myriad stars in the dark sky. He could see so well, so very clearly on this bright and crisp December night.

When Stephen lifted his wife on to the bed he felt the life pulsing through her. He felt Sarah's whole presence and vitality as he gently and skilfully loosened the lace of her nightdress. He looked at the outline of her perfect and alluring breasts. He looked at her twisted and wasted legs and he loved her.

'I'm sorry,' he said running his fingers through her long fair hair and kissing her on her cheek.

'I know,' she whispered, with an understanding smile. She had forgiven him a very long time ago. He brushed his lips softly against hers and he looked into her eyes. Her mouth opened slightly as if to say something. She looked up to search his face with beautiful blue eyes, glistening with emotion. He kissed her again, intimately this time, on her open mouth and she drew a sharp breath through her perfect nose. That night between those clean, fresh sheets he caressed and experienced her whole being; he received the warmth and truth of his beautiful and gifted wife with all her love and caring and he saw that, in real life, he had everything.

Y Mynydd

Man's main task in life is to give birth to himself, to become what he potentially is.
Erich Fromm

He was compelled by those coal-black eyes and smoky wisps of hair, wind-blown across the forlorn industrial face of his home town of Merthyr Tydfil – now known quite often simply as 'Merthyr'. As he looked down from the Aberdare Mountain, the March winds were still whining and carrying the sounds of clatter and thud from the foundry; it threw up so much flaming light that shadows swirled about the face of her landscape, and her startled eyes flashed on and off like beacons in the night. He was spellbound and he sought and chose words to express the enduring love he felt for the place of his birth, his life in his town.

The ominous clouds were congregating and hurrying across the sky as if to an important meeting of the fabled Gods. But he knew they would soon deliver their sodden message all across the head of the valley. So he savoured this moment as he reached out to her – his town. A windblown tear stung the scarlet of his icy cheek as he trembled and sighed breathlessly, saying,

'My town is on fire.' And he began to recite quietly his schoolboy composition:

The sun which served this lovely day
Has given way to a breeze
Forever I will wonder at the way
It feeds those hungry leaves

And the wind rushed and roared, cutting off his words.

He released himself, reluctantly, from the symbolic embrace in which his emotions held him and he hurried back down the mountain, through the sulphur-smelling streets of Georgetown, with the taste of soot in his mouth. The first signs of drizzle were on his coat and the dankness of communal sewage in his nose, as he opened the unlocked door of his one-up-one down miner's cottage where his weary wife waited with his meagre supper prepared.

The following morning, he was up at 5.00am for the morning shift, the miner's lamp hanging from his belt and bouncing against his strong thigh as he walked in the cold, smoky morning darkness to the train, which travelled through the tunnel under this, his mountain, to the Gadlys Pit in Aberdare. To pass the dirty drudgery of the dark, weary hours at the coalface, filling, emptying and refilling drams, he would relive the mountain walk of the evening before. It was the supporting cast to his wife's centre-stage embraces in the theatre of his mind's eye. And he would imagine his next rendezvous up here. Six days of the week in winter were dark days and nights, the shift starting and finishing in darkness, and so the approach of summer heralded the celebration of daylight hours.

These were his pleasures, and he saw poetry everywhere since Mrs Mary Thomas, his schoolteacher with whom he was infatuated as a child, had first introduced him to books and to the imagery of prose and verse. He did not like to go to the public houses, of which there were as many as chapels, because he had seen his mother drink herself to death. He had seen the drunks in the public house in which he had grown up, and he had seen them in the streets falling under trams and having limbs amputated. God knows, there were enough amputees from colliery accidents. He looked forward to the end of his shift, to the greetings of the children meeting the miners off the trains and begging for the remains of jam sandwiches made the night before from their snap tins, or 'Tommy-boxes' as they were known. And he looked forward to the hot bathtub in front of the fire. He was always careful not to wash the coal from the centre of his back, so as not to weaken the backbone, and he would eat his evening meal before his rendezvous up here on the Aberdare mountain overlooking his home town of Merthyr Tydfil – named from 480 AD after Tydfil the Martyr, a daughter of King Brychan of Brycheiniog (now Brecon), who was slain at Merthyr, protecting the town from the marauding 'pagan' Picts.

His early life had been difficult. He was only four years of age when his father, with his horse alongside him, was killed in the Cwm Ifor pit in the Rhydycar area of Merthyr. The following day his father was to have paraded his horse in the Mayday Parade. He remembered living with the dead body of his father in the tiny miner's cottage for the traditional three days and three nights. His mother remarried and he found himself living in the Narrow Gauge public house in the centre of Merthyr. The remarriage produced more and more children and, with each baby, he was further rejected and he began to see himself as an unwanted blemish on the face of humanity.

His capacity for loving was as great as his need to be loved. He loved nature and animals and poetry. He met his wife for the first time early one evening when he was strolling alongside the River Taff in Caepatnywyll. He was lost in a muse, reciting and practising aloud his own poetry when, to his surprise and embarrassment, he became aware of her presence. A young girl sat on the wall, watching him and smiling. He had tried to tell her why he was talking to himself, but the more he tried to explain the worse it became until they were both laughing, unembarrassed, as if they had known each other all their lives.

He could not have told her that his father was dead and that he had lived in a public house with his mother and stepfather. He could never have told her that his was a vicious stepfather who had knocked him about and that his mother had long ago rejected him for reasons that he could not understand. He had planned his departure from this terrible place he could not think of as home. He would leave the public house and go to his Auntie Doreen in Morgantown, his father's sister, herself a widow and in poor health. Doreen was in on the conspiracy and had no qualms about harbouring the boy.

In the meantime, he was learning fighting skills with some of Merthyr's best and building himself up at

Snow's Pavilion, the well-known boxing gymnasium at the bottom of town, in preparation for the day he would confront his stepfather and give him the beating he deserved.

Yes, he did. He left school at fourteen. He was up at five o'clock the following morning and in the Gadlys Pit in Aberdare by seven, having travelled on the Taff Vale Railway through the tunnel. He got home that night, a man. Six months later he had saved the money he needed. At the end of the week, after receiving his pay packet, he returned home from the morning shift at four thirty on a dark afternoon, his bags already packed. His stepfather began his usual warning threats of abuse, and he recited the words he'd rehearsed:

'You can only beat little boys; I'm a man now.' The stepfather, already stimulated by alcohol, went wild and ran at him with fists flying. That was his downfall. The younger man's sideways movement was too quick and his calculated hook smashed sickeningly against the side of the jaw, jerking the head violently. The stepfather crumpled onto the floor with blood spilling from his nose and mouth. He did not get up for a long time, and his jaw never properly healed. It was a constant reminder to him of his own brutality. Somewhere in the sordid filth of over-populated living quarters, his mother lay drunk. He never saw her alive again, because she died of a 'seizure' some weeks later.

He went back along the river the following evening after eating with his Auntie, and there she was again. She soon told him that her name was Lydia and her father was a minister of the church. His bruised knuckles were like a lingering bad taste, and he had derived little satisfaction from the evening before. He needed love desperately and so did she; her father was preoccupied with his position of importance in the community and with 'propriety' and, having no desire to demonstrate affection to anyone, not even his wife and children, he too was a tyrant in his own way. The couple fell desperately in love. They began to find secret places where they could be close, where they could experiment and express their love in as many ways as possible. It was never enough and, after almost two years of clandestine meetings and months of planning, they eloped to Aberdare where they were married in the registry by special licence. Doreen, his Auntie, was happy to accommodate the young couple until they could manage on their own.

Six months later, they were forced by Lydia's father to remarry in a Dowlais church. They were together and this was the most important thing in their young lives. Shortly after, the couple obtained a tied cottage of their own, in Georgetown, after he was transferred from Aberdare to the Plymouth Colliery in Merthyr. Doreen, for her part, was sad to see the young couple leave, but she was now in need of nursing care and she died a short time later in a fit of coughing. The couple were sad for their kind benefactor but had known all along that she was in much distress with a condition, which might have been tuberculosis.

That, my friend, was a long time ago here in Merthyr Tydfil, and I had to come back. Give us a hand a moment. I just need to get through this damned gate … never used to be one of these by here. Yes, it was a long time ago; and a happier couple you could never have known... She loved him more than words could describe; she did everything she could for him and he loved her. It took them nearly four years for her to become pregnant. She lost the first one before it went full term. Then she became pregnant again two and a half years later. Excuse me; got a bit of a sniffle coming on I think. Anyway, she died in childbirth. Yes, the child, too. Before she died, he sometimes brought his wife up here with him. That, my friend, was me. She was a good wife and I still think about what happened. Still, there's no use in all that now. Help me make it up the rest of the way just one more time. Well, I haven't reached her yet but I know I will. I just had to come back once more; I think I told you didn't I?

Oh, damn... I can't quite catch my breath. Better stop for a minute. It's a hell of a climb. Used to bring the dog up here; they called the village Penyrheol in those

days, short for Penyrheolgerrig. They call it Heolgerrig now; not a village any more either! ... That's better, press on up the hill. I've got to reach that place just once more ... there she is... early morning, quiet now. Funny thing, time has made her look fresher; lots of lush, green grass grown up around her. Look at those hairy wisps from the chimneys floating in the wind. Must be nearly sixty years ago I started coming up here, fancied myself as a bit of a poet then. I used to look out across there and say what came into my mind in my best words.

What do I see now? I feel that same enduring love for those coal-black eyes and smoky wisps of hair, wind-blown across the spreading face of the town of Merthyr Tydfil. As I look down from the  Aberdare Mountain the March winds still whine and blow the new green grass covering the colliery scars around the changing face of my town. I see estates of modern housing eclipsing traditional miners' cottages as they spread like spokes in a wheel from the town centre hub.

The old man seemed to be spellbound for a short while; he spoke some verse to me:

> *I walk my lanes of moonlight*
> *To find myself that peace*
> *Given by nature to the night*
> *Now that my day has ceased*
> *...then he left the mountain and soon he was gone.*

Ambition

I must keep aiming higher and higher even though I know how silly it is.
Aristotle Onassis

It was Sheila's beacon of red hair he'd seen first, then her unconditional smile and full figure as she had greeted him expansively, almost exuberantly, on his first day.

'Welcome to Wales, Martin,' she had beamed with a vigorous handshake, probably reserved for people who are especially welcome.

Martin had sensed the expectations they had of him. The department had been under pressure. The matronly team leader, known to everyone as 'Auntie Mary', had said to Martin at their introductory meeting that 'fringes of the Ystrad Estate seem to be turning nasty with more serious types of crime and ... well, I'm sure with your experience you've seen a lot of examples of what these things can do to people, families ... especially children.'

The interview had been straightforward. This parochial community in the South Wales valleys could benefit from Martin's impressive postgraduate-training and cosmopolitan experience in the City. Martin had wanted to make his mark but they were still using out-of-date methods of record-keeping and making far too many home-visits. 'Auntie Mary' was approaching retirement and out-of-touch with reality. The whole department had seemed hell-bent on languishing in this second-rate set-up with only two VDU screens between eight people!

The case conference had been a frustrating affair for Martin and he'd had difficulty holding his tongue. They didn't seem to know what to turn a blind eye to. In the City you didn't take any notice of 'soft' drugs; you dealt with the more serious matters. Then there was the one in the wheelchair – Gareth, the quiet one from the West of Wales somewhere where they still use the language. Nice enough chap but constantly over-identifying with families and individuals and finding mitigating reasons and some kind of rationale behind everything no matter how anti-social. They had all seemed preoccupied with 'background history', 'perspectives' and 'behavioural syndromes' instead of getting on with dealing with the real down-to-earth problems of people's everyday lives!

Martin had encountered surprising difficulty in adapting his city-acquired driving skills to the hilly and winding terrain. As he wrestled to co-ordinate steering wheel and pedals, Sheila briefed him about their home visit.

'Raymond Griffiths, the father, comes out of prison, marshalls his big family, takes up where he left off and leads them to the brink of disaster before returning to prison again and leaving them to sort out their wounded,' she had said, without taking a breath. The semi-detached slum was at the edge of an estate half-way up the mountain in a drizzle-hazed valley.

'That's par for the course,' Martin had replied.

'I'm worried,' Sheila had continued, 'that the four teenage sons are going to follow in his footsteps.' They had parked the car and scrunched the fine coal-carbon shingle underfoot as they climbed to the front door where Sheila had added breathlessly, 'You'll see a nine-week old over-fed baby ... the illegitimate child of their fifteen year old daughter Sharon.'

'I thought only mountain-goats and sheep lived up here,' Martin said, by way of introducing himself.

'They do, love,' was the eavesdropping trite reply from the dark within. The ample figure of Diane Griffiths had filled the corridor as she bustled back into the fag-ash squalor to resume her well-worn shiny sofa-seat. The baby peered suspiciously from behind a chocolate-smeared face and smelt of urine and stale excreta. Sheila had seemed at ease with the family and was told that the Community Health Nurse had just left. Martin had watched Sheila with some reluctant admiration and thought that, if they were to work together, they should talk socially later on.

'I've worked with this family for two years now,' Sheila had said on the more sensible and sedate journey back to the office. 'They're suddenly not as open as they used to be, and I'm worried in case they're getting involved in some way with drugs.' Martin had thought that he would soon find out. Nevertheless, he agreed to another joint visit with Sheila before taking over the case - Sheila having built up trust and empathy in her relationship with the family, of course.

He also suggested they could have a chat in 'The Red Cow' in Pontsticill that evening after the usual Monday afternoon team meeting. Sheila had suggested that Martin might also wish to talk with Gareth, who had some innovative ideas about working in these communities.

'In fact,' Sheila had said, 'Gareth has a lot of sensitivity and perception and seems to be able to ... I don't know ... get himself into their shoes before interpreting a situation.'

After the routine team meeting, they all met in 'The Red Cow'. Martin had made one or two recommendations as to how the Department could benefit from more progressive methods but sensibly reserved judgment on individual cases.

'I expect you'll see a difference in this type of environment, Martin,' Gareth had said wiping the beer froth from his moustache with his tongue. Martin had expected that the same principles would apply anywhere.

Gareth, minus his wheelchair for the evening, had offered his support to Martin and made a joke about Sheila's energy.

'She doesn't even stop when she's supping a pint!' he'd said affectionately. She wants to conquer the world ... solve everyone's problems in one swoop!' Sheila, with the bouncing chest and dark-brown, darting eyes, was the local girl made good. She had certainly seemed vibrantly attractive and alluring in those early stages of their new friendship. 'Never mind,' Gareth had continued philosophically. 'I often think it's important in this job to have something to be aiming for.'

Then he had said, getting into his stride and making a fisted gesture: 'It's my ambition, you know, to be able to walk from the office to the pub with a stick. What do you think of that then?' This, Martin had thought, was a distance of only about fifty yards. 'Don't know about getting back, mind you.' Gareth had said flippantly.

Martin had pondered quietly on his own ambitions and, a couple of pints on, had asked Sheila if she'd like to move on elsewhere. Sheila had explained that she was driving Gareth home. 'And we usually grab a take-away on a Monday. You're welcome to join us.'

Martin had been thinking. If the Griffiths family were at the centre of something, an unexpected visit from a streetwise city social-worker might uncover it. It was still only 6:30 in the evening and the smoky traces of the Griffiths family still remained in his clothing. He could put this 'social' time to better use than his new colleagues. He could also bring the benefit of his experience to bear and present Sheila with real insight instead of merely trying to make impressions of the family fit a syndrome or stereotype.

Then Martin could begin to introduce new methods of record-keeping and information technology. He had wanted ultimately to influence change whilst operating from a safe distance and a position of seniority. This was going to be part of a necessary process, he had told himself, of short-term sacrifice and hands-on work for longer-term gain.

There had been no answer and Martin had gone around and opened the back-gate. One of the sons had seen him through the back patio windows and, thinking he was an intruder, gone into the garden to challenge him. Martin had been in these situations before and he handled it well. He had been invited into the house and offered a joint. He had just left colleagues who were partaking of one socially-acceptable drug, he told himself, and what harm anyway. Besides, Martin was a new boy, an outsider, needing to be accepted by these people. Raymond Griffiths had returned from the club full of ale and had told everyone he just knew as soon as he'd heard about him that Martin would turn out to be one of the lads. Martin had felt good and warmed to both the familiarity of the situation and the task. 'This is the real heart of things,' he had thought to himself as, slowly, comfortably and consistent with his sharp-end experience, he had gained the superficial trust of the Griffiths family.

The protracted Court-proceedings had been attended by inordinate media attention and it hadn't looked good for the Department. Gareth, in particular, had perceived the situation sensitively. Both he and Sheila had referred independently to the background against which the whole episode was set, to the cultural differences and what was going on in the minds of the accused persons. They suggested other mitigating circumstances. But it had been a red-handed fair-cop. The package in question had been handed to an under-cover woman police officer at a motorway services and there really was no defence. It was bad luck, too, that Raymond Griffiths had battered the baby to death whilst junked-up on the stuff - plus or minus alcohol - it didn't really matter. He's in here somewhere too.

Gazing intently at the white, wispy travel-trails, set against the deep blue background of the summer sky, Martin bathes himself in the concept of interminable, clear, open space. He thinks about the rest of his life. He thinks about the unfairness of some people's lives and he thinks about life after death - especially in the aftermath of recent events. Most of all, Martin is experiencing strange new feelings. Amidst his remorse he is feeling pleased for someone else as he thinks about the big news of today.

Then there was Sheila - with all the energy and the heart of gold.

Today's a special day because Gareth and Sheila have been. They were full of reassurance about the future and of news of the various happenings in the office and on the 'patch'. As his dreams seem to fill the skies up above him, Martin can still hear Gareth's voice proudly and excitedly telling him, 'I walked to the pub with a stick last Monday ... what do you think of that, then?'

Mandy

'Sure, if I reprehend *anything in this world it is the use of my* oracular *tongue, and a nice* derangement *of* epitaphs!'
Spoken by Mrs Malaprop (mal a propos), a dubious wordsmith, in Sheridan's 'The Rivals'.

Just for once, I felt as if didn't have to worry about what I said. If only every day could be like yesterday. I mean, they just looked so glabberfasted I've never seen anything like it. Mind you, I knew what I was going to say to them if I ever got the chance. I'd reversed it over and over in my mind when I was sitting there checking off at the tills. I told them alright. I've got to be honest, I almost feel sorry for them now.

Anyway, Susie's Auntie Kate suggested I come down and have a chat with you imminently. Susie's my best friend and her Auntie Katie knows what to do; she said you deal with business presences and we read your divertissement about the business for sale. You see there's this money I'm going to inhibit and I've chucked my job in; I just walked right out of there after I'd given them a piece of my mind.

Why am I getting upset? I don't know really it's all just been a bit much, I suppose, and Susie's Auntie Kate says I'm over nought with it all. Yes, I'd love a cup of tea, two sugars. Susie's going round the shops and she said she'll come with Ron the Daevoo to meet me at your office. I didn't know she knew anyone called Ron with a Daevoo. Susie worked with me at The Con and they sometimes deplored us in the same jobs in the shop. I'm OK now, thanks; sorry. It's like Susie's Auntie Katie said, I was just a bit over nought with it all.

From the beginning, OK: I started working in The Con - oh sorry, that's short for *Economart*, the supermarket on Brecon Road. There's a name for a start – The Con. I mean, that's asking for trouble isn't it; a name like that. The Con, I ask you. Anyway I started there last September instead of going back to Bridgewood Apprehensive. My best friend Susie was already working there and she was the one who told me there was a job going. I took a load of GBH of the ears from Mum about not going back to school but Mum didn't have to put up with it, did she?

Susie and me, we were quite primate in school and kept ourselves to ourselves. When Susie left school and started work the other kids were getting on my tits … sorry, especially the bullies and it was hard for me to keep myself primate like I used to with Susie. In any case, these days you have to take unemployment when you can get it; never mind all this careers stuff they give you, not everyone wants to go to universality. I mean you have to have a lawn, and borrow money, and you might not even have unemployment at the end of it! Anyway Susie's Auntie Katie reckons I could have a chance to be on 'trupanur' or something. On trupanur – I don't know something to do with having your own business. She said you'd know all about being on trupanur. Yes, I know about business marriagement; we did domestic science at school and then I worked in The Con, didn't I?

My experience: when I started in the The Con I had a week of shelf-stacking before they put me in for training on tills. I had to do a test but I'd done GCSEs and didn't have a problem. Malaprop hated that. Somebody said Malaprop's been stacking shelves since Merry Evil times. Susie and me did 'The Rivals' in English and we named her after Mrs Malaprop who gets her words wrong. Malaprop in The Con always got hers wrong because she tried to use words that were a couple of sizes too big for her. Me and Susie of course both knows lots more words. We've both got a much better constabulary through doing English in school, and of course we knows how to mutilate them.

Everybody in Bridgewood Apprehensive knows 'The Con' because of that woman from the flats who was done for shop-fitting and it was in the news. Do you remember that? Anyway she used to be a celibated actress, this woman, and she'd lost all her money and had no sauces left at all. She died in the end, after the trial was all over. I felt really sorry for her; she always used to chat with me a lot when she came in. I think it was because I was the only one that really interfered with her. She was really nice but I always used to think she was a bit four-lawned and sad. I still say there was no need for that. I mean they didn't have to be funny about it did they? I mean it was nasty the way they vindicated her like that. I said I thought she couldn't help it and Malaprop tried to make out I might have been aiding and betting. I never helped customers with shop-fitting and the nearest turf counters is over two hundred litres away from The Con!

Anyway, from the time I started there, they seemed to be finding fault. If it wasn't one thing it was another. First off they had a go at me about my hair. Malaprop told me to cut it short or wear it up because I had to meet Jean Standards. I asked who Jean Standards was and Malaprop said I was trying to be far seeshus or something. Apparently Jean Standards is from the Viral Mental Health and she was coming to check our headwear. She didn't even look at mine. At least you could have a belligerent conversation with some of the teachers. Every time I needed change or ran out of money bags, Malaprop would come up and look at customers as if I had a bad arthroma all around me. If I needed a new till-roll you'd swear it was because I was a clapped out maniac! And you daren't make a mistake and put anything through the till twice with her around.

The money ... yes, I'm OK with figurines. We had to deal with money all the time in 'The Con'; Susie can't do figurines and so she had to stay on the shelves most of the time. We used to make a joke about it. We said it was infinitessimally worse than being 'on the shelf', you know, like when you can't get a husband and you're a sprinter for a long time. Anyway I was good with figurines. There was one man who said he'd given me a ten pound note for a flagon of cider and I knew he'd only given me a fiver. They had to switch off my till and count all the money. I reckon the customer just couldn't afford another flagon. There was no way Malaprop was going to miss a chance to make a fuss about it and she called down Billy Bunter, the Manager, and it all went from there. His real name's Mr Hunter but he suffers with old beastity and he's always being digestive with the girls. I'm pretty sure Malaprop heard him one time when he stopped me just between the Pampers and the frozen foods but she didn't say anything. Anyway the till balanced and the customer apologised and they couldn't fuss no more, so you see I know about figurines and tills and things.

Last Tuesday we went down to Susie's Auntie's after work. She's a real star is her Auntie Kate. She used to do a job like yours, something to do with business presences anyway. She used to tell us all spectifications and she said that's what I've got to ask you for ... not really sure why but you'll know all about that won't you. Oh yeah, the money. Well we were talking about Susie's money; it was held in a truss for a while and then she had it a couple of years ago. Her Auntie Kate said she thinks Susie should have divested with you in properties. Susie Palmer - lives in Terrace View. She spent some of it on some clothes and shoes. I think she said there were some other Sunday items or something, but she did say she'd put some by for a rainy day. Well it was raining on Wednesday ... No, I don't know how much but they knew about my heritance and they said it wasn't as much as I'm going to have when I'm eighteen.

Anyway I went home and talked to Mum about it. That was when she told me the secret she wasn't supposed to, because it could only be Dai Bulge later, and Susie's Auntie Kate shouldn't have been talking to Dai Bulge or something. I don't know Dai Bulge but she said there was money for me I wasn't supposed to know about until my eighteenth. She didn't even know it was my eighteenth this week. She definitely didn't know how much it was. As she said she divorced Dad when I was little more than a faeces in the womb. The executioner of the will was Uncle Joey, my Dad's brother, and he was always saying 'there's something we need to tell you when you're eighteen,' and I used to worry in case he was talking about the burks and the beasts – which of course I already knew all about. Anyway I went and asked him about it and he told me about how much money there's been in the truss for me since my father died. I couldn't believe it; it wasn't just the money but there was Dad's house he'd disinherited from my Gran. There were some divestments and life insurance, a bint-edge car he'd restrained and all on Sunday to be for Dai Bulge later he said.

So, next day I'm in there taking off my coat off first thing and Malaprop says something about me being unpunctuated again. That was it: 'I'm going to tell you something now in a minute,' I said, 'when I've got this thing off.' I was limpid and then I said. 'Were you just talking to me or have you got wind?' I heard someone say that on telly. She looked at me like she'd just pooped herself and then she just flew out of the door. By the colour on her face I thought she was going to have a colony or something. Mind you, she could have had wind because she was clutching her diagram. That wasn't the end of it. I'm sorting out my change and screwing in a new till-roll when over she comes with Bunter the Hunter and he says in his manager's voice, 'I understand, Amanda, that you've used some unpleasant words towards Mrs Bradshaw regarding wind.' I knew he was in a bad mood as soon as he said 'Amanda'. When he's on the creep it's always 'Mandy' but today it was 'Amanda'.

'And you needn't start neither,' I said. 'I've had enough of you an' all.' For once I couldn't think of anything else to say and there were customers coming in the shop. 'You don't give a monkey's about anyone!' I said, but I was getting a bit weepy. 'You don't care about anyone else and serve you right if you have got wind.' The trouble is I could feel all the motion welling up inside me and I wasn't sure about the money and not needing the job any more. Instead of just being fumigated and giving to them, I knew I was going to disinfect into tears and I wasn't going to show them that. So I just said: 'And I tell you what, you can stick your job up your rectangle!' and I ran out – forgot my coat of course.

I got home and started to panic and streak out about not having a job. Anyway, Susie came and digested me to ring her Auntie Kate. She told me to conflagrate with you because she'd seen your divertissement about ... hold on, I've kept it; I'll give it to you now in a minute. It says it's a 'business premises suitable for retail outlet', and Susie's Auntie Kate said, 'Why don't you go and see them because you really will be able to afford it and it could be your business.' We had a laugh but then it started to dawn on me that it really could happen and it might be a good idea. Uncle Joey says I'll be flushed. I know that means I'll have a lot of money. I never thought I'd hear myself saying that.

The money: they said 'The Soul Sisters' have got that because it's in a truss. No, I don't know who they are; perhaps they're family. Sounds like a pop group to me. I can have it when the reprobate's been. It's my birthday next week. I never thought in all my dreams it would turn out to be 'Economart' that was up for sale. The mind boggles. I told you, I've got to talk to Uncle Joey and The Soul Sisters. Funny, when you come in for some money everything gets complexicated. Do you know what I mean? I suppose you do. First thing I'm going to do if I buy it is change the name. 'The Con', I ask you. Thanks for the cup of tea; I can see Susie coming back from the shops. I can't believe it; that looks like Malaprop she's got with her. I suppose she's OK really and some of the kids from school around her as well. I wonder what they want. You know, it's nearly tea time but the day is getting better and better. I just want it to go on and on temporarily forever and never go to sleep. I can't wait to see their faces when I tell them.

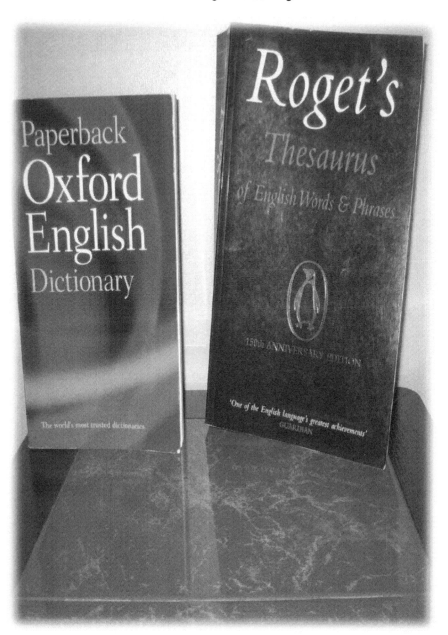

Deadly Dai

Everybody sets out to do something, and everybody does something, but most people don't do what they set out to do.
George Moore

You might well ask how I got in this state. Well it wasn't all my fault and if it hadn't been for... Well, best thing is for you to be the judge of it. What happened was like this: I decided to do some DIY on the outside of the house. I bought the supplies in: bag of sand, bag of cement and I stored it in the lean-to shed at the back of the house.

The first thing I had to do was borrow my neighbour's ladder to get up to the back bedroom window, which was stuck shut. I had to borrow my next-door neighbour's ladder because, when I tried to get up to the window without it, my foot went through the roof of the lean-to shed. There was only me at home; I couldn't get my foot out and I was stuck for half an hour. They definitely did not make roofs in those days as good as they do now.

Now, I've got to be fair, we're really lucky where we live because our nearest neighbours are very friendly and they said I could help myself to their ladder any time. The quick way across to my neighbour's garden is by climbing on the shed roof. Before you even think it, I did not put my foot through the hole in the roof on the way over to fetch the ladder. I was actually very careful to avoid the roof and climb over the wall. It was on the way back with the ladder that I forgot about the hole in the shed roof. Well, of course, I fell straight through the hole and into the shed taking the ladder with me.

I think I did tell you I'd stored sand and cement in there didn't I? Well it was right under where I fell through the hole. I ended up sort of upside down with my legs tangled in the roof. Not only that, the door was locked from the outside. I felt a bit like Houdini, I tell you and, worse still, the ladder was already half way across the wall between the two houses.

When the whole of me and one half of the ladder went through the roof, the other half of the ladder was leaving next door's garden in a sort of catapult action and my neighbour who owns the ladder had hung a bucket from the end of the ladder on a piece of rope. As I descended through the roof into the lean-to shed the other end of the ladder flew up launching the bucket into the air and into a trajectory which took it high over the top of my garden.

On the other side of our garden and lying in the bucket's target area, is my other next door neighbour's garden. Thankfully it just missed his greenhouse. Unfortunately, my next door neighbour's wife was hanging out the washing and she was not paying proper attention and she failed to notice this missile in time.

Now I could not see from where I was, but my next door neighbour's wife has alleged she was hanging out the washing one moment and had a bucket on her head the next. Not only that, the bucket contained some gooey sort of white stuff – I think the man from the fire brigade called it bonding. I couldn't see anything much because I was busy tying myself safe but I could hear this terrible screaming.

I'm told that bonding is a kind of adhesive – glue, in other words. Now the bucket handle was attached to some rope so that my neighbour (whose ladder was responsible for all this) could lift stuff up to the top when he was working. Once again, going by what I've been told, it was this very same rope which caught on a bra-strap and wound around the clothes-line. As the clothes-line swung back and fore, so did my neighbour's wife, who was now sitting in the washing basket. Now you might remember that this bucket and rope were at the other end of the ladder to which I was still clinging in the lean-to shed. As she swung back and fore, so did I, one of sand, one of cement alternately slowly descending deeper and deeper.

Well, I seemed to have been upside down trying to pull my head and shoulders out of this sand and cement for ever when I heard this siren and I think to myself, 'Thank goodness; the emergency services are coming to get me out of here.' Anyway, the siren wasn't for me; it was for my neighbour's wife - whose new hairdo I think looks absolutely fine. My neighbours on either side aren't speaking now but I've forgiven them both. And you should have heard what they said about the nasty fright I had, through no fault of my own.

What happened to me? You might well ask, as I said to you right at the start. There I am, dangling upside down in the shed with the door locked and my feet still caught up in one end of the ladder which, in turn is stuck in the roof. I couldn't shout because, every time I tried, I had a mouthful – one of sand and one of cement alternately. And it started to rain. There was a big hole in the roof and I was starting to get visions of my head and shoulders being removed at a later date like a bust of Alexander the Great.

Now I've dealt with the neighbours either side but, right at the end of my garden, are my other sort-of neighbours whose back garden backs onto ours and ours backs on to theirs, if you get my drift. Now, they've got a dog that tends to wander. This dog is a sort of mongrel who I've worked out would be about a hundred and thirty if he was human. He's very friendly and we've become mates. Unfortunately his hearing and his sense of smell are also about a hundred and thirty and he thought I was calling him. Oh, yes and his eyesight is also about one hundred and thirty and he didn't notice the hole which had caused all these problems. When he landed on top of me, he did notice there was something not quite right and he started to bark like a canine geriatric in distress.

My very nice neighbours whose garden backs onto ours were really apologetic when they saw all the trouble their dog's wandering had caused me and they agreed to pay for the damage to the roof of the shed. Oh yes, and not to worry about the window and that little bit of brickwork, he'll do it for me (the neighbour not the dog), being as I'm not quite one hundred per-cent.

At least he could understand what a nasty shock I'd had.

The Loot

A Letter of Thanks to Gaynor, my wife Sheila's lifelong friend who, in true Olympian fashion, also tolerates me as a friend and who, in about 1998, tried to rescue me from the following self-imposed `scatterbrain' crisis.

Dear Gaynor,

Thanks for your help in trying to locate the plumber's cash - six hundred-and-fifty quid of it - last Wednesday evening. Herewith the full story, which I owe you permission to dine out on.

On Monday morning prior to your generous intervention, Sheila and I placed the aforesaid six-hundred and fifty quid in cash - hereinafter referred to as *The Loot* - in a sealed envelope marked 'Plumber'. On Monday evening, the plumber not having collected *The Loot*, I telephoned him and explained that I would be not be here the following day, Tuesday, because I had an appointment in Cardiff on that day.

'Hold on to it, Dave,' said the plumber, being a trusting sort of fellow. 'Hold on to it and I'll collect it on my way home on Wednesday evening.' This would, in fact, have been around the same time that I came to be telephoning you for assistance in finding *The Loot*. As you know, I was convinced it was in a book somewhere in the bookshelves to the right-hand side of the rather nice traditional fireplace which we like very much.

On Tuesday morning I had to call at the Merthyr Tydfil Library to collect my short story prize cheque (for *The First Time, Cyfarthfa 1997*) – hereinafter referred to as *The Prize*. Quite sensibly, I had been concerned about leaving *The Loot* in an unoccupied house - even in a secret place amongst the books, for example. After all, who's to say there isn't a literary burglar in the locality? So I decided that my next stop, after the Merthyr Tydfil Library and en-route out of town, would be 'Chez Plumber'. I placed *The Loot* safely in the inside pocket of my 'Lieutenant Columbo' coat - hereinafter referred to as *The Mac* - and the expedition was underway.

The visit to Merthyr Tydfil Library to collect my Short Story prize cheque - hereinafter referred to as *The Prize* – swelled me with such pride and levitated my thinking to such a high place, I think it might have been the emotive impact of this diversion which then caused my memory to lapse. In short, I forgot to call at Chez Plumber and drop off *The Loot*.

I caught the bus to Cardiff, where it can be difficult to park, and headed for the building society to deposit *The Prize*. I have never understood why Alliance and Leicester Building Society promptly closed down their Merthyr Tydfil branch when I came to live here but this coincidence did occur. After waiting in the queue at a Cardiff branch of the Alliance & Leicester Building Society for a short while, I discovered that I had in fact, after receiving said treasure, left it in the Merthyr Tydfil Library.

I left the queue having failed to consummate the transaction. I went outside to find it was now raining quite heavily so I called at Howells Department Store to purchase an umbrella. Others seemed to have realised the same need and I had to wait in a small queue. I found myself, once again, in the position of having queued unrequitedly. I had forgotten to get some money whilst visiting the Building Society. My memory having got me into this embarrassing situation, it then played the unusual trick of remembering something. It remembered *The Loot* - still burning a hole in *The Mac* which, of course, I was wearing. When I protested, my memory (complete with horns this time) said, somewhat impatiently, 'You've got to go to the Alliance & Leicester Building Society later. You can replace anything missing from *The Loot* then.' By this time I was at the front of the queue. I tore open the envelope and explained to the two shop assistants that this was the plumber's money. They're not very chatty at all these days, these young shop assistants. They just looked at each other, wrapped up the umbrella, and gave me my change.

I arrived next at an Italian restaurant where I had agreed to meet friends who had been there for some time already. When I explained that I had left *The Prize* in the car, they didn't seem terribly surprised and made a remark to the effect that neither Dave West nor Prince Charles is required to carry money – which I think, in retrospect, was probably a little rude. Anyway, it was resolved that we might as well have lunch before collecting *The Prize*. After all, I had opened the envelope now and it was not as if I didn't have plenty of money on my person. I could then go to the Alliance & Leicester Building Society, restore *The Loot* to its original total, all would be well with the world and nobody – Sheila, that is - need ever know of my indiscretion.

A bottle of wine later, the world was a wonderful place, the chef had assured me that the whole of Italy could be mine tomorrow, the Italian Restaurant seemed to have moved to a different area of Cardiff and the Alliance & Leicester Building Society was shut!

I was conveyed to a public house in Caerphilly where my friends rendered themselves unfit to drive. I began to wonder how I would get home and, indeed, whether it was a terribly good idea to go home. I then found myself in the cab of an industrial vehicle (a kind of truck driven by an obliging pub regular who had just finished work), trying to rendezvous with Sheila somewhere between Caerphilly and the A470 Cardiff to Merthyr road. I'm sure said truck driver exaggerated when he described me as hanging out of the window with arms flailing whilst trying to be noticed by Sheila who was travelling in the opposite direction on the dual carriageway. There was, he said, some concern lest I left a cascade of twenty-pound notes streaming out of *The Mac* which, partly supported by an umbrella, was flapping flag-like in the slip-stream of said truck.

Back at home, I decided to tell just a little white lie about *The Loot* and to hide it in a place different to the usual one. I did this so that everyone – Sheila, that is - could be spared the anxiety of knowing that I had been on the loose in Cardiff with the Plumber's six-hundred and fifty quid on my person.

I don't know about you, but liquid dietary supplements and my memory just do not get on well together. The memory in question did me no favours whatsoever the following day, Wednesday; it went almost completely absent and only had a vague inkling that *The Loot* might be somewhere amongst about four hundred and fifty books – either to the right or the left of the fireplace or in another bookcase somewhere else in my study. It was in this desperate set of circumstances that I rang you requesting some greater acuity than I seemed able to muster. Despite your possessing this to far greater advantage than me, we failed to locate *The Loot,* my indiscretion was revealed and the rest I suppose is history.

Many thanks for your help and for not (to repeat your own terminology) 'battering me': an action which I am now aware you expressed a pressing desire to carry out. It is a true friend who comes, at the drop of a hat, to try to locate *The Loot* in the wrong place.

Since Sheila located *The Loot* - fifty quid short - in the LEFT-HAND bookshelves, she has taken charge of the Building Society Pass Book, *The Prize* and, of course *The Loot*, the plumber has been paid and I probably won't have any favours associated with matrimony until my birthday - which will be in excess of another seventeen weeks from the time of writing.

Author Profile

David has always worked with people and been fascinated by their lives; his experience includes RAF service; teaching; criminology and public health. From his late teens, he wrote short stories and poetry. He has dealt with the anguish, anxiety, damage and depressions of bipolar disorder: a price paid for impassioned, creative periods when he has felt 'touched with fire'. Having won a local competition with a short story, he has had further success including publication locally and in national magazines. He is also currently in the process of writing a novel, a comedy script and a children's book.

Publisher Information

Rowanvale Books provides assisted self-publishing services to independent authors, writers and poets all over the globe. We deliver a personal, honest and efficient service that allows authors to see their work published, while remaining in control of the process and retaining their creativity. By making self-publishing services available to authors in a cost-effective and ethical way, we at Rowanvale Books hope to ensure that the local, national and international community benefits from a steady stream of good quality literature.

For more information about us, our authors or our publications, please get in touch.

www.rowanvalebooks.com
info@rowanvalebooks.com

Printed in Great Britain
by Amazon